RAIN

In the lap of the storm clouds—the rain comes—
Its hair loosened, its sari borders flying!
—Rabindranath Tagore

RAIN

Sudeep Sen

with

Twenty Contemporary Indian Artists

Gallerie

*Mapin*Lit

AN IMPRINT OF
MAPIN PUBLISHING

First published in India in 2005 by
Gallerie Publishers
208 Om Chambers, Kemps Corner
Mumbai 400 036. India
gallerie@vsnl.com • www.gallerie.net

in association with
MapinLit/Mapin Publishing Pvt Ltd
31 Somnath Road, Usmanpura
Ahmedabad 380 013. India
Tel: 91-79-2755 1833 • Fax: 2755 0955
email: mapin@icenet.net
www.mapinpub.com

Simultaneously published in the
United States of America in 2005 by
Grantha Corporation
77 Daniele Drive, Hidden Meadows,
Ocean Township, NJ 07712
mapinpub@aol.com

Cataloguing in Publication Data
SEN, SUDEEP, 1964 —
Rain
I Title; II English Fiction/Poetry;
III Indian Fiction/Poetry; IV World
Literature; V Indian Art; VI South
Asian Art; VII World Art / 821'.9'14

ISBN: 81-901999-0-0 (Gallerie)
ISBN: 81-88204-60-9 (Mapin)
ISBN: 1-890206-88-1 (Grantha)
LC: 2005926925

Distributed in North America by
Antique Collectors' Club
Tel: 800 252 5231
email: info@antiquecc.com
www.antiquecc.com

Distributed in the United Kingdom,
Europe and the Middle East by
Art Books International Ltd
Tel: 44 (0) 207 953 7271
email: sales@art-bks.com
www.artbooksinternational.co.uk

Distributed in South-East Asia by
Paragon Asia
Tel: 662-877-7755
email: rapeepan@paragonasia.com

Distributed in the rest of the world by
Mapin Publishing Pvt. Ltd.

Cover & Frontispiece:
A. Balasubramanium
Author photo: Priti D. Sen /
AARK ARTS
Design: Bina Sarkar Ellias
Processing: Pragati Art Printers,
Hyderabad
Printing: Ajanta Offset, New Delhi

for

Joseph Brodsky (1940-1996)

Nobel Prize for Literature 1987

and

Aria, Sara & Sarina

The First Octet

The Second Octet

The Only Sestet

Banquo: *It will rain tonight.*

First Murderer: *Let it come down.*

—William Shakespeare, *Macbeth*, (III.iv.24)

She faded, like a cloud which had outwept its rain.

—Percy Bysshe Shelley, *Adonais*

THE FIRST OCTET

RAIN, MAPS

It has started raining—sharp shards of transparent sheets hit the glass of the window that threatens to crack, but upon meeting its surface, melt to water. There is a constant blur of water outside. It is a curiously inviting scene, one that seems misty with flickering crystals glowing in parallel striations—the patterns changing their tack depending on the wind's mood-swings.

I look at this grand show of rain everyday and everyday I weave a different pattern, both due to my own mood and the weather's inherent currents. Each day I weave a little piece, adding a patchwork to this infinite quilt, one that buries unwanted narratives in the warmth and cosy of its apparent comfort.

The way the quilt's colour and imprint form are unpredictable. The only thing that is known is the exact square-inch space that each segment will add up to. Its individual design is unknown until it is stitched onto the larger stretch of linen. It is a journey, mapping a route that is largely undecided, perhaps even unknown.

I like this mystery. It allows one to completely imagine and plot a path that suits one's own sense of direction. I have a compass to find the Earth's cardinal points. But this is of no use when it comes to details of terrain, temperature, vegetation, and the unexpected inhospitability of travel itself.

I like the unknown, the unpredictable, the sense of encountering the virgin, even though the path might have been traversed before. But I do not have that knowledge, so it is entirely fresh, untrammeled, and personal. I begin walking.

I can walk anywhere from almost anywhere. I do not need timetables, or ports of embarkation and disembarkation. I do not need guidance of the tourist

trade, or the help of someone who has done it before. I just venture out; let my legs do the walking, my eyes do the seeing, and my heart do the navigating. And amid all this, my mind keeps me company, as I imagine, dream, and see—visual and virtual, spontaneous and sure.

LANGUOR, WET

A typical start to a Kolkata day, more like an extension of last evening. The quality of light is the same as yesterday's—deep grey with an immense cloud over-hang. The electric lights inside are still on, as though they weren't turned off last night. There is a heavy, brooding, damp quality in the air that seems to invisibly wrap my exposed skin. My hair feels humid—even the upholstery, the clothes, and the trapped house-air.

I step out into the back garden. The soil is clayish and waterlogged. The plants look prosperous and overgrown though the lack of sunshine today does not highlight the clarity of fresh green. The insects, caterpillars, and spiders are busily getting on with their business, entirely unperturbed.

Barek, our guard and gardener, sits outside under the drive's front-porch pondering what to do. He has a perennial uninterested look that transforms to a semi-bright spark whenever any of his employers are in sight. There is a lot he could do, but he does very little, blaming his inactivity on the weather.

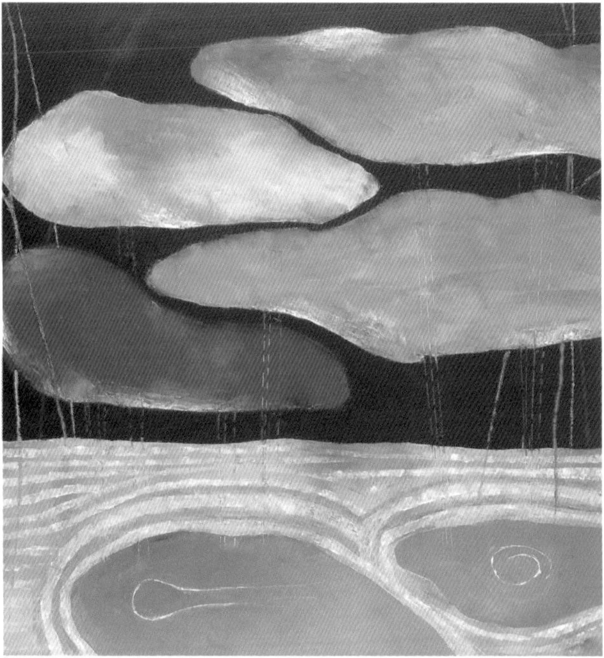

RAIN, RAIN

It is another space, another view, but the same rain. It has been raining all of last night through to this morning. It changed to a drizzle for about twenty minutes before resuming its full fury. But in its fury, there is an overbearing sense of surety and steadiness of intention. There is a constancy with which the water pelts down the striated streams of liquid.

It is hot and muggy, though clear—one of those slow languorous days, deceptive because it looks hopeful and bright at the outset, but the moment one attempts to do anything, it starts raining and a heavy soporific lull sets in.

FERN FROST

In front of my desk, the glass panes on the window are frosted—but the temperature inside is not freezing. Outside, the tropical pre-rain humid-heat of the afternoon makes the sight of broad-leafed palm trees an epitome of brooding languor, and plenitude.

The air in my study is cool, perhaps even conditioned cold, relative to the heat outside. Plain acts of physics and geometry make simple sights alter their guise; change from one state to another, even though that may be transitory.

There are definite mathematical equations to corroborate such sights,

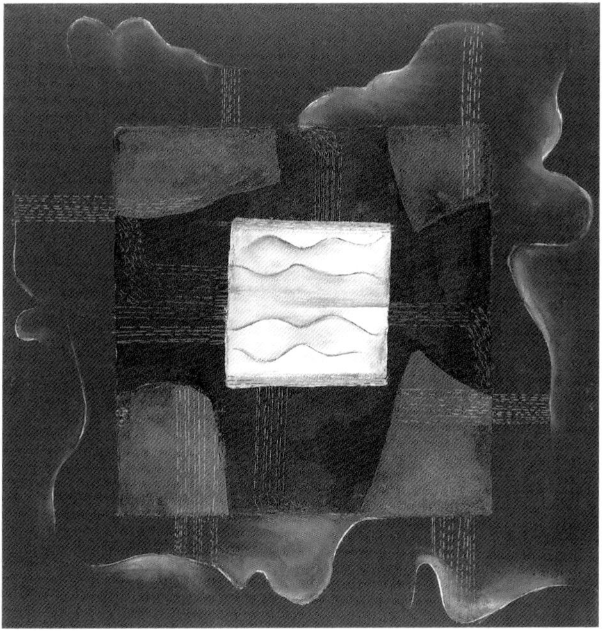

well-tested algorithms—but for me, illusions provide more room for imagination than the exact state of space.

The palm leaves outside are huge, enormous, like large fern-sails, their edges defined by the crisp 'cut-n-stitch' along their invisible seams. Their strength and dignity must come from the elegance of their trained spine.

All this is much like the gaze of a sophisticated onlooker—a visualiser—who sees the same scene with a different sense of calm, poise, thought, and imagination.

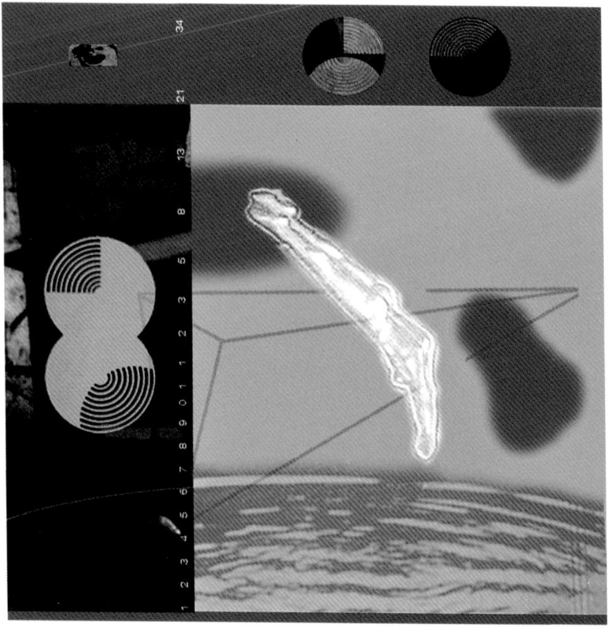

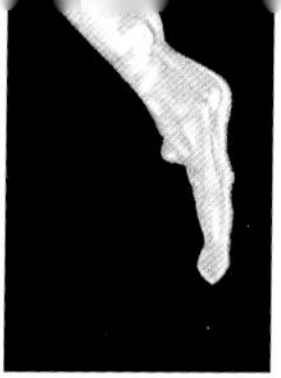

AIR-CONDITIONER, RAIN

Isolated amid the air-conditioned comfort, vast well-cleaned concrete spaces, and the shelter of tropical profusion, I feel completely cut off from the hustle and bustle of metropolitan living I have been used to for decades.

It is cold in this room. The temperature belies the climate of the external topography and terrain. It is this chill that keeps me awake, otherwise the dull humidity of the outside's dead heat induces an infectious sleep.

It is raining again, but today's is a beautiful kind of rain—steady, symmetrical, confident, and unobtrusive. It has a kind

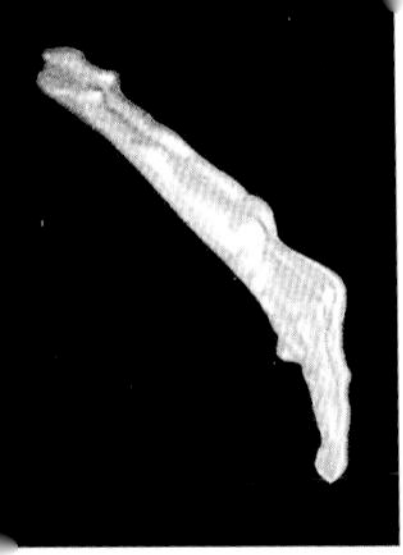

of presence that is omnipresent without actually announcing that it is there, like 'ambient' music, though that would be too cruel a comparison. Somehow technological similes used to compare elements in nature are always fraught with dubious results.

I work here having lost the sense of time and its own presence of metre. Somehow natural syllabics have their own quiet momentum, one that leads you forward, setting their own pace and mapping their own space, much like the process of breathing itself.

Natural breath pace and its pauses

have always been crucial to my own
sense of textual pacing, the way they
wind and twist displaying their curious
unpredictable intentions.

HEAVY METAL

Ship-breakers, snake-like in a single-file, slither towards monumental vessels stuck aground in the rain-swept muddy delta. This is Gujarat's heavy metal graveyard, where abandoned big queens of the high seas are left to reminisce about their past glamour and glory.

Most of these workers are day-labourers—each, like a foot-soldier in an ant march, is an emaciated cog in the giant flesh-and-metal machinery—most of them untrained in dismantling thick sheets of steel. Their mud-coloured bodies glisten, as their gleaming sweat and the acrid water's viscous reflection in the marsh-pool threaten to boil over in the sun.

But there is hope—hope for a colony of people earning a temporary meagre living—hope for the virgin soil to mingle with the poisoned rust of the ships so that both can learn the effect of contamination—and hope too for an onlooker for images that propel creativity.

The ships stand, rain-soaked, statuesque in spite of their exposed dismantled skeletons. Bit by bit, they will be further broken down and sold for scrap metal, and many of their fixtures will be sold as display items in brass and antique shops in the big cities.

Scrap metal never held such fascination and beauty in my eyes before. In spite of this wet panorama's unconventional composition—the scene somehow had a haunting quality of expansiveness that defied the obvious imagery of labour, extortion, and death.

MONSOON GREENS

Green is the colour most visible to me
these days—glazed-oil green, light-banana
green, olive green, dry green—the green
myopia of politicians, the green armoury
of warfare, the green undergrowth—
all twisted and weed-like, green and
unstable, and no one in sight to prune
or train them.

Shades of verdure had caused a blinding
effect on my system. Trendy herbalists are
wrong—instead of a soothing, calming
effect, green has a peculiarly vulnerable,
nausea-inducing effect on me.

Green bile and vomit, a Frankenstein-
fantasia, green mucous cough spat by

tuberculosis patients, green moss
and grime in unclean toilets and
storm-drain ditches that line the roads—
beautiful green, awful green, healthy
green, wet green, monsoon green.

Monsoon has arrived—persistent in
intent, green in jealousy. The rain is
going to be around for a while,
only hastening and never dampening
the insidious, monochromatic,
chameleon-spread of green.

BENGAL RAIN

Rain has sparked so many imaginations all over the world. But there is nothing like the rain in the two Bengals—West Bengal in India, and Bangladesh.

Rain in its overbearing gait, its preparation, its stature, its brooding quality, and its romantic heavy-lidded cloud structure. Ordinarily one would call these rain clouds 'cumulonimbus', but that name or model does not in any way do them justice.

Here the clouds assume a deep grey-black quality, and just prior to a heavy down-pour it is almost pitch-dark. The leaves rustle around in little circular flurries, there is a pregnant heaviness in the air, the smell of wet clay and the hustling sounds of birds taking shelter permeate the sky.

Barsha, as the monsoon rains are locally known, has a truly unmatchable resonance—elegant, weighty, ponderous, raw, but always striking and graceful.

It was not raining rain to me,
It's raining violets.
—ROBERT LOVEMAN (1864-1923), 'April Rain'

rain
came down in slanting lines.
—ALEXANDER SMITH (1830-67), *A Life Drama*

THE SECOND OCTET

RAIN CHARM

Another rain-swept day leaves everything water-logged—ponds, drains, streets, and rivers—everywhere water is overflowing. The green blades of grass in the garden lie submerged under a rippling shallow sheet of water. Through refraction, they take on magical underwater seaweed shapes. Except here, the grass is evenly cropped, so it appears as a glazed woven mat of wet-green. Rain has also left the plants and trees gleaming, bursting in plenitude.

Natural irrigation in excess creates its own slow rot, a sublime slime of wet decay and birth, profusion and irresistibility. Rain has this special seductive appeal—its innocuous wet,

its piercing strength, its gentle drizzle-
caresses, its ability to douse and arouse.
The entire charm lies in its simplicity.

RAINING RAIN

rain rain rain rain rain rain rain rain rain rain rain
rain rain rain rain rain rain rain rain rain rain rain
rain rain rain rain rain rain rain rain rain rain rain
rain rain rain rain rain rain rain rain rain rain rain
rain rain rain rain rain rain rain rain rain rain rain

rain rain rain rain rain rain rain rain rain rain rain
rain rain rain rain rain rain rain rain rain rain rain
rain rain rain rain rain rain rain rain rain rain rain
rain rain rain rain rain rain rain rain rain rain rain
rain rain rain rain rain rain rain rain rain rain rain

rain rain rain rain rain rain rain rain rain rain rain
rain rain rain rain rain rain rain rain rain rain rain
rain rain rain rain rain rain rain rain rain rain rain
rain rain rain rain rain rain rain rain rain rain rain
rain rain rain rain rain rain rain rain rain rain rain

rain rain rain rain rain rain rain rain rain rain rain
rain rain rain rain rain rain rain rain rain rain rain
rain rain rain rain rain rain rain rain rain rain rain
rain rain rain rain rain rain rain rain rain rain rain
rain rain rain rain rain rain rain rain rain rain rain

rain rain rain rain rain rain rain rain rain rain rain
rain rain rain rain rain rain rain rain rain rain rain
rain rain rain rain *raining violets* rain rain rain rain
rain rain rain rain rain rain rain rain rain rain rain
rain rain rain rain rain rain rain rain rain rain rain

rain rain rain rain rain rain rain rain rain rain rain
rain rain rain rain rain rain rain rain rain rain rain
rain rain rain rain rain rain rain rain rain rain rain
rain rain rain rain rain rain rain rain rain rain rain
rain rain rain rain rain rain rain rain rain rain rain

raining violets

NIGHT RAIN

I woke up at 3 a.m. with a start. I was shivering and sweating profusely at the same time. The cotton tee-shirt I had on was completely drenched. So was the bed-sheet I was lying on.

Outside I could hear the rain hitting the terrace floor with relentless ferocity. Thunder-claps shook the glass panes to near breaking point.

I love the sound of water and rain whatever their mood. It has a certain sense of assurance, a steadiness that isn't always present in the other elements.

I had a spontaneous desire to step out into

the rain. I was drenched anyway, so getting the rain's feel on my back would do me no harm. Besides, getting wet in the night rain has its peculiar thrills.

I stepped out—my body heat met the rain. The rain-water sizzled off my skin steaming up in curls of white vapour.

All I could see and imagine was a blanket of hoar frost that enveloped me and the rain. Night rain camouflaged in the steam of body heat.

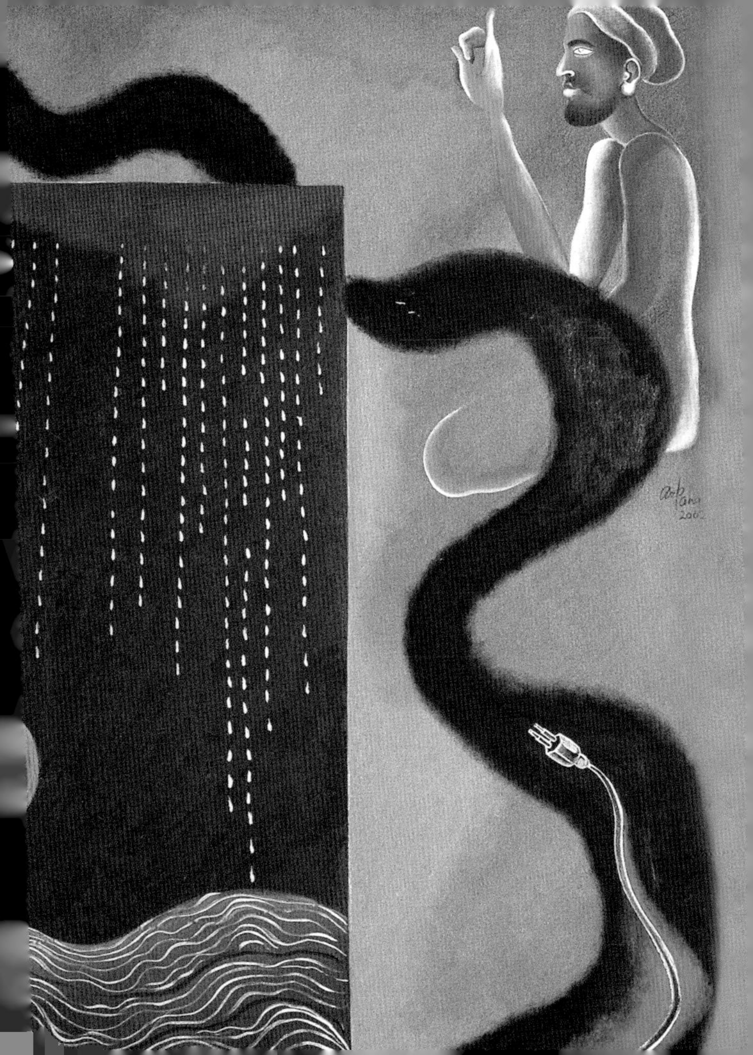

LONGING, RAIN

The very last drop of rain perched on the
edge of her navel—the last bead of sweat
balanced on the feather of her eyelash—

the last long-wet of my kiss on her skin—
all these demand more, more, more—
more wet, more wet—

yearning for more rain, fire, desire,
moisture—and the cool chill of
crystal-water, thirst, saliva, longing, rain.

SHOWER, WAKE

The September showers came too late,
giving ample time for a prolonged
drought. But when they eventually
arrived, they brought with them the full
fury of an unstoppered monsoon—the
rain pelting down hard, cracking open
newly-laid tarmac, exposing the earth and
the elements once again.

The pouring water persisted, overflowing
until everything was affected—weak roofs,
power lines, trees, unwarned people,
shelters—almost everything.

After two weeks, the storm subsided—
a war-struck wet wake lay shattered in
the aftermath, hungry, heavy, and low like

polluted clouds of mist over a submerged *mofussil* that was trying to breathe and periscope back.

But here, the arteries are severed too severely to recoup their strength anytime soon. With or without water, in flood or drought, existence here remains unchanged.

RAIN, DESIRE

The heavy sediment of South Indian
espresso sinks—in a deliberate silent-slow-
motion thud—to the bottom of my glass
mug. My head is infused in swirling
aromatic fumes that wrap the morning's
fresh-green rains. Moisture's deep taste
defies my body's intention to stay dry.

It is cloudy—deep grey and about-to-
burst—they over-hang teasingly, arching
their backs, pregnant with wet's
many-prismed face—merely seconds
short of relief.

Everything around is still dry,
though the damp's constant warning
makes me wait—tentative, unsure

when the cloudburst would release all its heat.

But imagining the rains can be far better than relentless rain itself. At least one can control its intensity of downpour, wind, force—imagine its desire, definition, and direction.

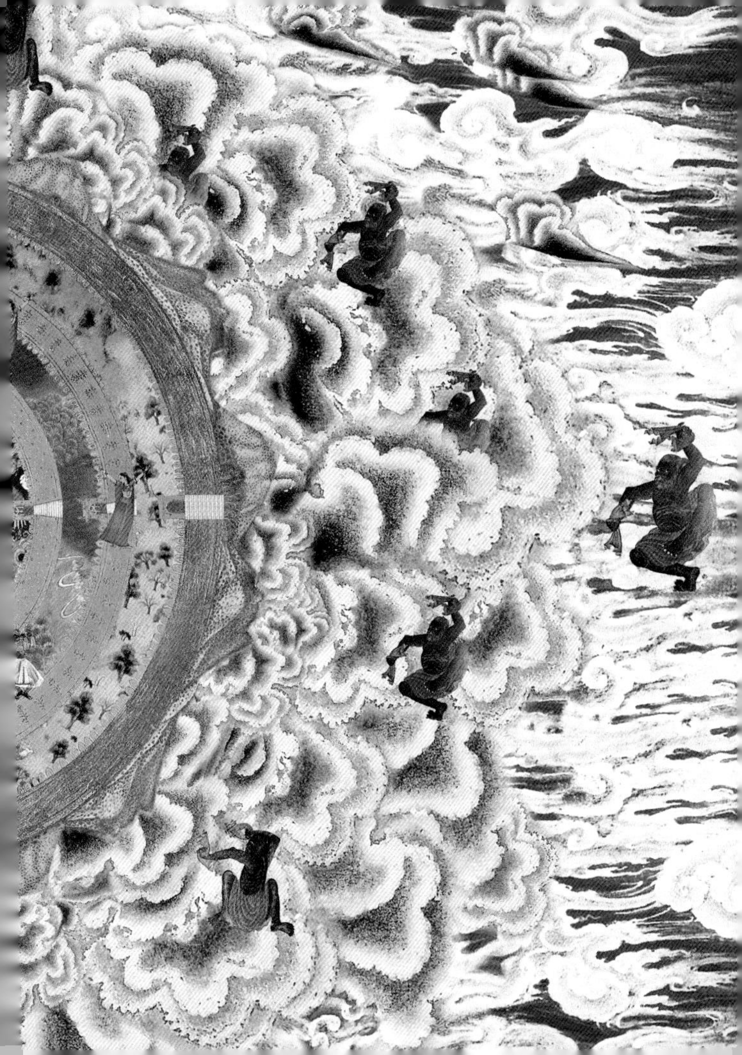

WANT, EAGER

Summer's dead heat—humidity teasing
the clouds to shed rain—absolute
stillness—every leaf balanced, though
quivering, tentative—eager to feel the
moisture on their skin.

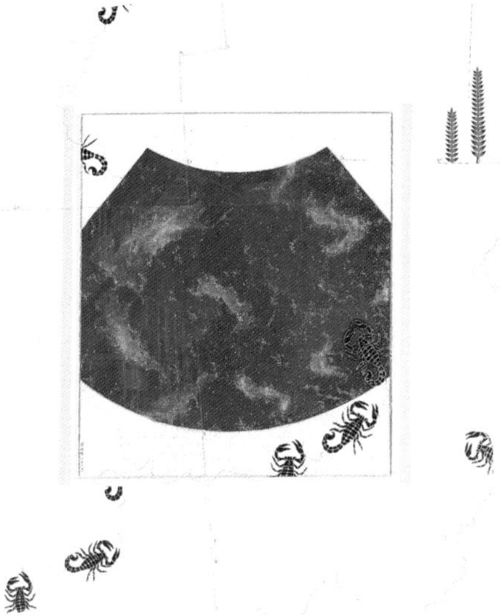

OFFERING, FLUIDS

The kindness of libation, lyric, and blood.
Her endless notes left for me—little secrets,
graces, trills recorded on blue and purple
parchment to be lipped, tasted, devoured—
only the essence remains, its stickiness, its
juice, its memory—

Seamless juxtaposition—the brute and the
passion, dry of the bone and wet of the sea,
coarseness of the page and smooth of the
nib's iridium—

I try to trace a line, a very long line—the ink
blots as this line's linear edge dissolves and
frays—like capillary threads gone mad, twirling
in the deep heat of the tropics—threads
unraveling, each sinew tense with the want
of moisture and the other's flesh—

There are no endings here—only beginnings—precious incipience—translucent drops of sweat perched precariously on her collarbone, waiting to slide, roll unannounced into the gulleys that yearn to soak in the rain—

Heartbeats shift the shape of globules as they alter their balance and colour, changing their very point of gravity—constantly deceiving the other—

I stand, wanting—wanting more of the bone's dry edge, the infinite blur of desire, the dream, the wet, the salt, the ink, the rain, and, the underside of her skin—

It is perseverance that makes the difference between seduction and courtship.

—THE I CHING

The more you know, the less you need.

—AUSTRALIAN ABORIGINAL SAYING

THE ONLY SESTET

MORNING, RAIN

Buried deep in warm skin—toasted in
the night's long passion, I struggle this
morning—to emerge out of this heavy,
rain-filled air.

RAIN, KISS

A languorous kiss—the faintest smell
of rain and ocean—salt-lipped breeze,
pleading—

RELEASE, RAIN

The stamen raises its head—bursting,
to shed pollen—relief-rain showers—
the parched folds of pink skin.

DRIZZLE, CLIMAX

Lips of a rose-bud open—to let the dew
drop in—

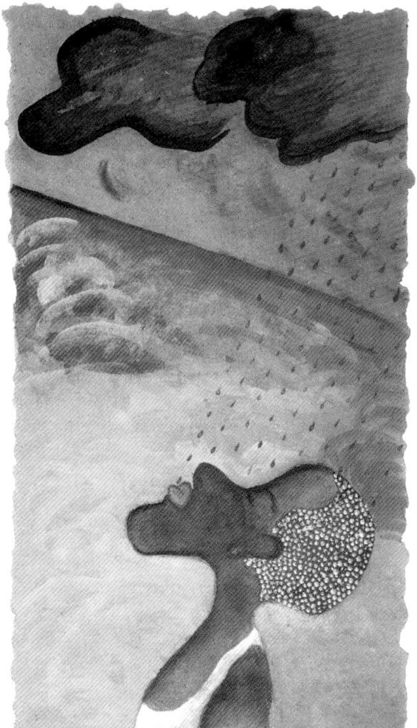

The famous Nal Sarovar near Ahmedabad which

DROUGHT, CLOUD

It is bone-dry—I pray for any moisture
that might fall from the emaciated skies—

There is a cloud, just a solitary cloud
wafting perilously—

But it is too far in the distance for any
real hope—for rain.

The famous Nal Sarovar near Ahmedabad which plays host to migra

every year has gone completely dry – *Javed Raj*

KNOWLEDGE, NEED

"The more you know, the less you
need"— but that is not true at all for
thirst, water, or rain.

Sabavala

ACKNOWLEDGEMENTS & PERMISSIONS

Many of the individual pieces in this book, some in earlier versions and under different titles, appeared in the following magazines, newspapers, journals, books, and the internet. My thanks to the editors and publishers in the UK, USA, and South Asia, who first commissioned and published them. They include: *Independent*, *Observer*, *Daily Star*, *Six Seasons Review*, *Aark Arts Review*, *British Council Quarterly*, *Literary Review*, *London Magazine*, *Van Gogh's Ear*, *Prague Literary Review*, *Gallerie International*, *Indian Literature*, *The Little Magazine*; and in the following books: *Lines of Desire* (USC, 2000), *Postcards from Bangladesh* (UPL, 2002), *Perpetual Diary* (Aark Arts, 2002), and, *Monsoon* (Bengal Foundation, 2002).

My heartfelt thanks to—Bina Sarkar Ellias for her enthusiasm and passion for my written word, her friendship, and for elegantly designing this book—to Rafeeq and Tom for their friendship and bonhomie—to Pallu for being an omnipresent hand and computer angel—to Savita for gastronomic pleasures—to Polly Gilbert and Firdous Azim for their keen editorial eye—and finally, as always, to Priti and Aria for providing the inevitable sense of calm.

—*Sudeep Sen*

I thank all the artists for giving me permission to reprint their work from *Gallerie* [Vol.6, No.1, 2003] for this *Rain* book.

—*Bina Sarkar Ellias*

Some Works by Sudeep Sen

Poetry/Prose

Leaning Against the Lamppost; The Lunar Visitations; Kali in Ottava Rima; New York Times; Parallel: Selected Poems; South African Woodcut; Mount Vesuvius in Eight Frames; Dali's Twisted Hands; Postmarked India: New & Selected Poems; BodyText; Retracing American Contours; Almanac; In Another Tongue; Lines of Desire; A Blank Letter; Perpetual Diary; Postcards from Bangladesh; Monsoon; Prayer Flag; Distracted Geographies; Rain.

As Editor

Lines Review Twelve Modern Young Indian Poets; Wasafiri Contemporary Writing from India, South Asia & the Diaspora; Index on Censorship Songs [Poems] of Partition; The British Council Book of Emerging English Poets from Bangladesh; Midnight's Grandchildren: Post-Independence Contemporary English Poetry from India.

The Author

Sudeep Sen [www.sudeepsen.com] was born in New Delhi. He studied literature there and in the USA. As an Inlaks Scholar, he completed an MS from the Graduate School of Journalism at Columbia University in New York.

He has written, translated & edited over a few dozen books and chapbooks. Winner of many international and national prizes, he was awarded a Hawthornden Fellowship (UK) and nominated for a Pushcart Prize (USA) for poems included in *Postmarked India: New & Selected Poems* (HarperCollins). More recently, he has published *Postcards from Bangladesh, Monsoon, Prayer Flag, Distracted Geographies*, and edited an important landmark anthology, *Midnight's Grandchildren: Post-Independence English Poetry from India*.

His writings have appeared in the *Times Literary Supplement, Guardian, Independent, Financial Times, Evening Standard, Scotsman, Scotland on Sunday, Herald, London Magazine, Poetry Review, Literary Review, Harvard Review, Prague Literary Review, Times of India, Statesman, Observer, India Today, Outlook, Gentleman, Indian Literature, Biblio, Little Magazine*, and *Indian Review of Books*, among others.

As an invited author representing his country, he has read his work worldwide, and has been translated into several languages, including: Arabic, Bengali, Czech, Finnish, French, German, Greek, Hebrew, Hindi, Hungarian, Italian, Japanese, Korean, Macedonian, Persian, Romanian, Slovenian, Spanish, Swedish, and Turkish.

Sen has been an international poet-in-residence at the Scottish Poetry Library in Edinburgh, and a visiting scholar at Harvard University. He is the editorial director of AARK ARTS; is on the editorial boards of *@las*, *The Journal of Commonwealth Literature*, *Orient Express*, *New Quest*, and *Six Seasons Review*; and is an associate of *The Paris Review*.

The Designer

Bina Sarkar Ellias is editor and publisher of *Gallerie*, the international arts and ideas journal that has won over 9 international and Indian awards for excellence in 7 years. Its patrons include leading international art galleries and museums: The Tate in London; The Museum of Modern Art and The Metropolitan Museum in New York; The Smithsonian in Washington; besides Harvard, Boston and other universities. Her work has been recognised through grants by The Prince Claus Foundation in Holland, The British Council in India, and the Government of France.

She has designed catalogues for Swiss artist, Aaron J. Wegmann and Indian artists, Jehangir Sabavala and Rekha Rodwittiya, and the 40th Anniversary catalogue for Gallery Chemould, 'crossing generations: diVERGE', 2003, besides books for artists like Tyeb Mehta and Chinthala Jagdish. She has also curated 'Rain', an art show in Mumbai and has been invited to the Glasgow New Moves Festival of the visual and performance arts, to give a talk on her work.

She has written for *The Times of India*, *The Indian Express* and *The Hindu*, and has edited *Fifty Years of Contemporary Indian Art*, 1997 for the Mohile Parikh Centre, Mumbai.

Altaf studied at St. Martin College in England. He has had solo and group exhibitions in India and overseas. He organised several workshops sponsored by Xal Praxis. As principal of the New Habib High School, he had worked on several educational projects.

A. Balasubramanium took a Bachelor's Degree in painting and printmaking from the College of Arts and Crafts, Chennai. He has also studied printmaking in Edinburgh and Austria and received numerous awards in printmaking, including the Charles Wallace India Trust Award, the Grande Prix at the World Print Festival, Yugoslavia, and a gold medal at the Egyptian International Print Triennale. He has had solo shows in India, Spain, Austria and the US and UK and has participated in group shows at other international venues. Bala, as he is popularly known, lives and works in Bangalore.

Sujata Bajaj received her Masters Degree in painting in Pune where she took her PhD as well. In 1988, she received a scholarship from the French Government to study at the Ecole Nationale des Beaux Arts, Paris. She has also worked at Studio Claude, Viseux, Paris. She is the recipient of several awards including the Bombay Art Society Award and the Maharashtra State Art Award. She has had shows in India, UK, France and Norway. She lives and works in Paris.

MANISHA GERA BASWANI received her Bachelors and Masters Degree in Fine Art from the Jamia Milia University, New Delhi. She was granted the National Scholarship from the Government of India 1991-93, as well as a French Government Scholarship to visit Paris in 1993. She has participated in several shows including ones at Chennai, Mumbai, New Delhi and at the Schoo Gallery, Amsterdam, 1995. She lives and works in New Delhi.

MEERA DEVIDAYAL graduated with English Literature from Kolkata, 1966 and was a part-time student at the J.J. School of Art, Mumbai, 1971-74. She has had solo shows in Mumbai, New Delhi and Baroda and has participated in several group exhibitions. She lives and works in Mumbai.

ARPANA CAUR is a self-taught artist whose main concern has been the condition of women in India. Her major solo and group shows include the Algiers Biennale, 1987, the

Glenbarra Art Museum Exhibition, 1987, the Lalit Kala Academy, '79 and '93, the City Hall Gallery, Ottawa, Canada, 1981 the National Gallery of Modern Art, New Delhi, 1986. She lives and works in New Delhi.

JOGEN CHOWDHURY studied at the Government College of Arts and Crafts, Kolkata. His works have been exhibited in several shows, including the I, III and IVth Triennales in New Delhi, 1972, '75 and '78, the Sao Paolo Biennale, 1979, the IInd Havana Biennale, Cuba, 1986, Festival of India, Geneva, 1989. He lives and works in Shantiniketan.

JATIN DAS studied painting at the J.J. School of Art, Mumbai. He is a recipient of many awards including the award of the 4th Bharat Bhavan Biennale. He has participated in several solo and group shows in India and overseas, including the Paris Biennale, 1971 and the Venice Biennale, 1978. In 1991, the Lalit Kala Academy held a Retrospective of his works. He lives and works in New Delhi.

BINA SARKAR ELLIAS has doodled since she could hold a brush and pen. These have often found their way into her journals. She lives and works in Mumbai.

CHINTHALA JAGDISH received his five-year diploma in painting from the JNT University, Hyderabad, 1978, and a two-year post diploma in mural design at the MS University, Baroda, 1980. His scholarships include the British Council and Charles Wallace India Travelling Grant for study on Henry Moore in Britain. He has also received The Pollock-Kresner Foundation Award, 1993, New York besides several prestigious national awards. He currently lives and works in Hyderabad and Michigan.

PARESH MAITY received his Bachelor's Degree in Fine Arts from the Government College of Arts and Crafts, Kolkata and his Masters Degree from the College of Art, New Delhi. He has received the award for the best water-colour painting from the Government of West Bengal and the All-India Fine Arts Society. He has participated in a number of group shows in India and at international venues, including the Cleveland International Drawing Biennale, 1995. Maity lives and works in New Delhi.

GAUTAM MUKHERJEE is a self-taught artist. He received the gold medal at the Kanagua Piennian World Art Exhibition, 1997, and was awarded as the Chief Artist at the Centenary

Celebrations of the AICC, Mumbai, 1985. He has had several group and solo shows in India and overseas. He lives and works in Mumbai.

BAIJU PARTHAN studied painting at the Goa College of Art and received a post-graduate diploma in Comparative Mythology at the University of Mumbai. Parthan has had several successful shows in India, China, Germany and the UK, besides participating in various group shows in India. Baiju lives and works in Mumbai.

GIEVE PATEL is a general medical practitioner. He received the Woodrow Wilson Fellowship, Smithsonian Institution, Washington D.C. in 1984, and the Rockefeller Fellowship from the Institute of Cultural Consciousness in South Asia, University of Chicago in 1992. His works have been shown in the Royal Academy, London; The Museum of Modern Art, NY; and the Grey Art Gallery, NY. He lives and works in Mumbai.

REKHA RODWITTIYA received her degree in Fine Arts from the MS University, Baroda in 1981; and her Masters from the Royal College of Art, London for which she received the Inlaks Scholarship. In 1990, she was conferred the Staff Fellowship of the Rockefeller Foundation Asian Cultural Council to work in the US. She has held solo shows at the Gallery 678, New York, and the Studio Barbiere, Venice. She has also participated in the IInd Biennale of Havana, Cuba. She currently lives and works in Baroda.

JEHANGIR SABAVALA completed his Diploma from the J.J. School of Art, Mumbai, 1944. Subsequently, he attended the Heatherley School of Fine Art, London, 1945-47, the Academie Andre Lhote, Paris, 1948-51, the Academie Julian, 1953-54 and the Academie de La Grande Chaumiere, 1957. He won the Padmashree Award in 1977 and was awarded the Kala Ratna by the All India Fine Arts and Crafts Society in New Delhi, 2001. He has shown at several prestigious shows including the Venice Biennale, 1954, the Commonwealth Arts Festival in London, 1965, and the Indian Fine Arts Society, Singapore, 1999. He lives and works in Mumbai.

PARITOSH SEN studied at the Government College of Arts and Crafts, Chennai in 1942 and at the Academie Andre Lhote, the Academie de La Grande Chaumiere, the Ecole National des Beaux Arts, and the Ecole du Louvre, Paris between 1950 and '53. He founded an artists' group called the 'Calcutta Group'. His works have been exhibited at the Commonwealth Festival in London, 1965 & 1986, Sao Paolo Biennale in 1965, and the Havana Biennale in 1986. Sen lives and works in Kolkata.

HAKU SHAH received his Bachelors Degree in Fine Arts from the MS University, Baroda in 1955 and his Masters in 1959. Setting up a folk art museum in Ahmedabad, he conceived and designed a multi-art-and-crafts complex at Udaipur called Shilpagram. He won the Rockefeller Grant in 1968 and has held several solo shows in India and overseas. He has been associated with the Museum of Mankind, London, and the Tropical Museum. He lives and works in Ahmedabad.

GULAMMOHAMMED SHEIKH received his Masters Degree in painting from the Faculty of Fine Arts, M.S. University, Baroda. He won the Padmashree Award in 1983. A Visiting Artist at the Art Institute of Chicago, 1987, and Artist-in-Residence at the School of South Asia Regional Studies, University of Pennsylvania, he was one of the founder member of the 'Group 1890' and has held numerous shows in India and abroad. He lives and works in Baroda.

Cover & Frontispiece: Untitled, 2003. Detail. 50x50 cm. Acrylic & acrylic sheets. A. Balasubramanium

Page 1: Rain, 2005. Mixed media. Sudeep Sen

Pages 9, 41, 69, 79: Illustration. Watercolour on paper. Bina Sarkar Ellias

Page 10: Bund, 2003. Detail. 140x54 cm. Mixed media on paper. Sujata Mehta

Page 14: Untitled, 2003. Detail. 112x112 cm. Acrylic and oil on canvas. Jayashree Chakravarty

Page 18: The Clouds Crowd 1, 2003. 60x60 cm. Oil on canvas. Haku Shah

Pages 20, 21: The Clouds Crowd 2, 2003. 60x60 cm. Oil on canvas. Haku Shah

Page 22: Above. Untitled, 2003. 50x50 cm. Acrylic sheets and wax. Below. Untitled 2003. 50x50 cm. Acrylic and acrylic sheets. A. Balasubramanium

Pages 24, 25, 26: Silver Cloud, 2003. 120x120 cm. Acrylic on canvas. Baiju Parthan

Page 29: A Rain of Fire, 2003. 91.5x60 cm. Oil on canvas. Altaf

Pages 34, 35: Couple with Umbrellas, 2002. 91x152 cm. Oil on canvas. Paritosh Sen

Pages 37, 38, 39: Untitled, 2003. 32.5x80 cm. Watercolour on paper. Paresh Maity

Pages 43, 44, 45: Untitled, 2003. 74x27 cm. Acrylic on paper. Untitled 1, 2003. 55x49 cm. Acrylic on paper.

Gautam Mukherjee

Page 49: Untitled, 2003. 180x120 cm. Acrylic and oil on canvas. Rekha Rodwittiya.

Pages 52, 53: Crossing the Rain, 2002. 145x206.5 cm. Oil on canvas. Arpana Caur

Page 54: Wet in the Rain, 2003. 76x56.5 cm. Watercolour on paper. Jatin Das

Page 57: Varun, 2003. 38x49x16 cm. Papiermache. C. Jagdish

Page 58: Man in the Rain with Bread and Bananas, 2001. 150x82.5 cm. Oil on canvas. Gieve Patel

Pages 61, 62, 63: Conjuring Rain, 2003. 63-95 cm. Gouache on inkjet print. Gulammohammed Sheikh

Pages 64, 65: November Rain, 2003. 45x40 cm. Gouache on sikishi board. Manisha Gera Baswani

Pages 68, 70, 72, 73: May God Have Mercy, 2003. 150x90 cm. Oil on canvas. Haku Shah

Page 74: Rain Lover, 2003. 50x30x70 cm. Terracotta. Shyamal Ray

Page 76: Rain in Shantiniketan, 2003. 56.2x71.2 cm. Ink with brush and pastels. Jogen Chowdhury

Pages 80, 82, 83: Megh Malhar, 76.5x101 cm. Mixed media on canvas. Meera Devidayal

Pages 84, 86, 87: The Darkening Air, 1962. 61x107 cm. Oil on canvas. Jehangir Sabavala

I had published my most intimate, and quietly personal book, *Monsoon*, in 2002. At the time, I could never predict the public response of what was essentially an understated, literary and artistic enterprise for me. For many years now, I have been writing about the rains in its various guises—set in the big cities of the world: Kolkata, Delhi, Mumbai, Chennai, Goa, Dhaka, Bogotá, San Juan, Istanbul, Johannesburg, Seoul, Edinburgh, London, New York—as well as set in their more fleshed out overt versions in bucolic surroundings in South Asia and elsewhere.

Ever since *Monsoon* was published as a special edition in Dhaka, it has garnered glowing reviews there, in India, Europe, and the USA, in spite of the book being sparingly available in the last three places. Friends and admirers of the book here have urged me to produce an Indian edition so that it could be readily and affordably available here.

"Rain came bubble-wrapped in the guise of a little book. The pages awash with its wetness of words and images, unfurled a torrent of thoughts, some of which became this issue (of *Gallerie*: Volume 6, Number 1, 2003). *Monsoon*, [with] the poet and photographer's exquisitely crafted words and images, inspired *Gallerie*'s 'Rain'," wrote the editor, Bina Sarkar Ellias, in the preface of that special issue. That issue (apart from carrying some of my pieces from the book itself) also contained commissioned artwork on rain by leading Indian artists. Buoyed and braced by both *Monsoon* and the 'Rain' issue's positive critical response, Bina and I decided to join hands as writer, artist, designer, publisher and friend, to bring the book out again in an altered *avatar*.

There are significant differences this time around to the point that it is almost a new book. *Rain* is set in an entirely different format and size, and with a completely changed and re-imagined visual emphasis, philosophy and scope. The first duotone *Monsoon* edition carried my text along with black and white photos of a Bangladeshi photographer that I had chosen and curated. This *Rain* edition is in full colour and concentrates purely on works created by contemporary Indian artists, thereby acting as a visual complement to my words.

I thank all my friends, co-artists, sponsors and publishers who have made this wonderful venture possible. I especially thank Bina for her warmth and for taking this on as the first *Gallerie* edition of book titles. I hope that the readers too, as we did, enjoy through the pages of this book, the Indian subcontinent's most enigmatic and seductive season—the monsoon rains.

—SUDEEP SEN

New Delhi / Monsoon 2005

Beauty of style and harmony and grace and good rhythm depend on simplicity.

—PLATO